CHARLIE BROWN

VIOLET

SHERMY

PATTY

LINUS

SNOOPY

LUCY

'PIG-PEN'

SCHROEDER

THE WONDERFUL

WORLD OF PEANUTS®

Selected Cartoons From
more PEANUTS®
VOL. 1

by Charles M. Schulz

A FAWCETT CREST BOOK

Fawcett Publications, Inc., Greenwich, Conn.
Member of American Book Publishers Council, Inc.

THE WONDERFUL WORLD OF PEANUTS

This book, prepared especially for Fawcett Publications, Inc.,
comprises the first half of MORE PEANUTS, and is
reprinted by arrangement with Holt, Rinehart and Winston, Inc.

Eighteenth Fawcett Crest printing, February 1970

Published by Fawcett World Library,
67 West 44th Street, New York, N. Y. 10036
Printed in the United States of America

ARE YOU GOING TO NURSERY SCHOOL THESE DAYS, LUCY?

YES, I'VE BEEN REINSTATED

IS IT FUN?

IS IT FUN?! ALL WE HAVE TO DO EVERY DAY IS PLAY PLAY PLAY PLAY PLAY PLAY...

I'VE NEVER BEEN SO BORED IN ALL MY LIFE!

SCHULZ.

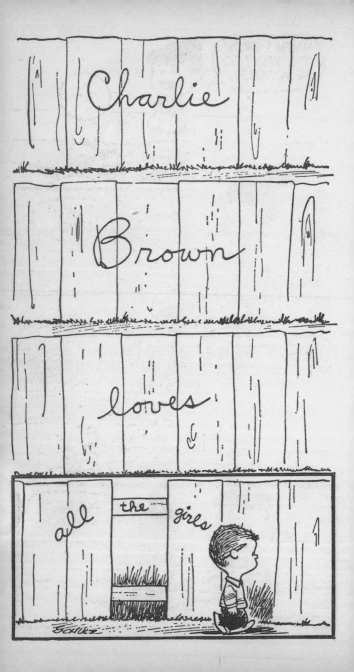

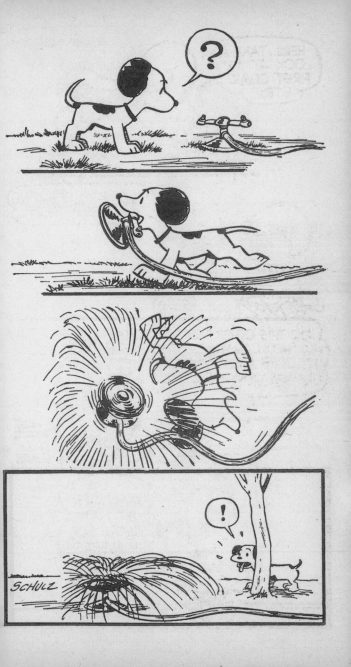

SHERMY!